BY THE SAME AUTHOR AND ARTIST

The Bible Storybook

The Nursery Storybook

The Good Shepherd Storybook

The Amazing

Bible Storybook

Georgie Adams *Illustrated by* Peter Utton

Orion
Children's Books

For

Ian Butterworth—G.A.

Maureen Budner and Carolynn George,
the St Edwards School Library—P.U.

First published in Great Britain in 2001
by Orion Children's Books
a division of the Orion Publishing Group Ltd
Orion House
5 Upper St Martin's Lane
London WC2H 9EA

Text copyright © Georgie Adams 20001
Illustrations copyright © Peter Utton 2001
Designed by Ian Butterworth

Georgie Adams and Peter Utton have asserted their right to be identified
as the author and illustrator of this work.

A catalogue record for this book is available from the British Library

Printed in Italy by Printer Trento S.r.l.
ISBN 1 85881 663 7 -

Contents

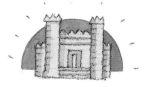

Foreword

*T*he *Amazing Bible Storybook* is a collection of favourites from the Old Testament – exciting and mysterious stories about God and his people. In *The Beginning of All Things* is the Creation, the mystery of God at work making the world and everything in it. There are great stories about Moses such as *'Frogs, Flies and Locusts!'* and *'Crossing the Red Sea'*, full of drama and adventure. You'll find two spies and some strange battle plans in *'Joshua and the Battle of Jericho'*, and be amazed by *'Strong Man Samson'* who pushed a temple down! You can read about the wisdom and wealth of King Solomon, and travel with the Queen of Sheba who rode a thousand miles just to meet him!

There are psalms too, poetic songs written long ago in praise of God. The much-loved *Psalm 23* describes God as a good shepherd who looks after his people and protects them from harm, while the message in *Psalm 148* is for every living thing to 'Praise God'.

Remember that all the events written about in the Bible happened a very long time ago. Even before these stories were written down, people had been passing them from one family to another for hundreds of years, retelling them over and over again.

And here I am now, telling them for you, adding my own thoughts and ideas, to bring people and places to life. But the original spirit of these stories is still there, so I hope you'll enjoy reading them . . . and will find 'something amazing' in every one!

Georgie Adams

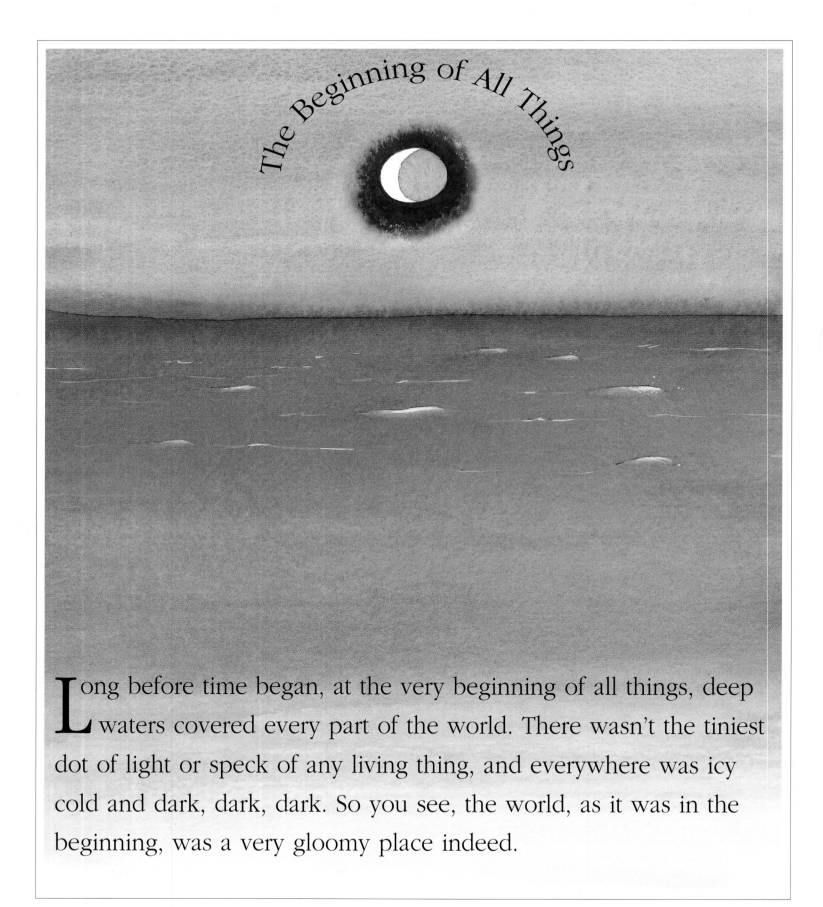

The Beginning of All Things

Long before time began, at the very beginning of all things, deep waters covered every part of the world. There wasn't the tiniest dot of light or speck of any living thing, and everywhere was icy cold and dark, dark, dark. So you see, the world, as it was in the beginning, was a very gloomy place indeed.

Can you imagine what it must have been like? It's not easy. Shut your eyes and try. For a moment all is quiet. Then you begin to hear sounds of life; a door bangs, a dog barks or a car goes by on the road. And, just when you're trying your hardest to think about nothing . . . a telephone rings! With so much going on around you, it's difficult to think of a time before anything or anyone existed.

The Bible says only God was there at the beginning. He took six days to make the world and fill it with wonderful things. We may not know exactly what 'a day' means in God's special time. It is a mystery. Only God can say. You'll find 'The Story of Creation' all about the making of our world, in the very first book of the Bible.

The First Day God began work, creating the world. He said, "Let there be light." And there was! A brilliant light broke through the darkness and spread over part of the world. God called the light part 'day' and the dark 'night' which together made one whole day. We split our days into parts called 'hours', and know that it takes twenty-four hours to make one whole day.

Then evening passed and morning came.

The Second Day On the morning of the second day, God looked at the world. There was water – oceans of it – everywhere. "Let there be sky over the waters," he said. So that was done. In no time, billowing clouds were drifting across the heavens.

The Third Day God created dry land. He ordered the oceans to roll back and, where there had been water, mountains, hills and deserts appeared. "I'll call the water 'sea' and the land 'earth'," said God.

To begin with, nothing, not even a blade of grass, grew anywhere. The earth was bare until God said, "Let all kinds of plants grow." And they did. Vegetables, crops and flower seeds sprouted; trees grew up and made great forests. God looked at what he had done and was pleased. Already the world was looking a much better place!

The Fourth Day At night time the sky was inky black. So God thought there should lights to brighten the darkness. He made the moon and stars to shine at night-time. He made the sun to warm the earth during day. These two great lights in the sky, the sun and the moon, give light to our world. The sun helps plants to grow, and marks the four seasons of the year – spring, summer, autumn and winter.

The Fifth Day God saw the sea sparkling in the sunlight. The sea looked splendid but . . . it was empty. There wasn't a living thing in it or in the sky above. "Let the sea be filled with fish," he said. "And let birds fly in the air."

So on the fifth day, the first living things came into being. Big and little fish swam in the oceans; birds flocked together and flew overhead. Soon the sound of birds singing could be heard all over the world.

The Sixth Day Next God made animals of all kinds to live on the earth. It wasn't long before there were many strange and beautiful creatures living in the jungles, deserts, mountains and fields. From big beasts to tiny ants . . . God made them all.

But the best part of God's creation was still to come. On this, the last day God worked, he made human beings. He made a man called Adam and a woman called Eve, who became Adam's wife. God said Adam and Eve should love one another and take good care of all the animals he had created. God told them to obey him, and try to live the way he wanted them to.

Then God spoke to every living thing he had made; Adam and Eve, the birds, the fish and all the animals. He told them to make homes and begin families of their own. In time, God knew there would be enough people and creatures of all kinds to fill the world.

On *The Seventh Day* God rested. He said it was to be a special day for everyone – a time when people should rest from work, and enjoy the world he had made.

The Prince, the Shepherd and the Burning Bush

Do you remember the story of Moses, the baby in the bulrushes? His mother nursed him until he was old enough to go and live in the palace with the Egyptian princess, who had adopted him.

The princess loved Moses. She gave him the very best clothes to wear, and servants who would do whatever he asked. He was treated like a real prince in every way. The princess's father, the king, or Pharaoh as he was called, had many wives and children living at the palace. So Moses would have had plenty of young friends to play with.

The Egyptians were clever people and learning was important to them. Moses was taught the alphabet, and how to write with a pen and ink on papyrus. He learned to read and count too. Moses worked hard and was good at his lessons, and he grew to be a wise young man.

Although Moses had been brought up as an Egyptian, he never forgot he was an Israelite. Israelites were people who believed that there was only one God whereas others, such as the Egyptians, worshipped many gods. Moses often thought about his parents, his brother Aaron, and sister Miriam, living near the River Nile. Sometimes, while he was riding in his chariot Moses would see his own people working as slaves, building fine temples and pyramids for Pharaoh. Moses watched them heaving massive stone slabs into place, and sweating in the scorching sun. The cruel Egyptian slave-drivers beat them with sticks to make them work faster. It made Moses sad to see them treated so badly.

One day, as Moses was out walking, he saw a slave-driver beat an Israelite to death. That did it! Moses was *so* angry, he killed the Egyptian bully with his bare hands. Then he looked around. Moses couldn't see anyone about and *thought* he was alone. Thinking no one had seen what

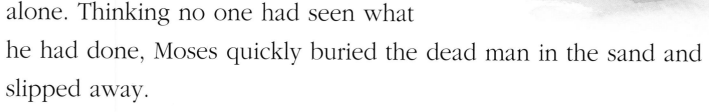

he had done, Moses quickly buried the dead man in the sand and slipped away.

Next day Moses came across two Israelite men quarrelling. They argued fiercely and began punching each other.

"Stop!" cried Moses, pushing the two men apart. "You shouldn't be fighting. You're both Israelites!"

The man who had started the argument looked at Moses and sneered.

"Well, what are you going to do about it?" he said. "Kill me, like you killed that Egyptian, yesterday?"

Moses was horrified. So, someone *had* seen him after all. He was in big trouble! It didn't take long for the news to spread and, when Pharaoh heard about it, he ordered Moses to be punished. Moses knew that if he was caught he would be put to death. That was the law.

There was no time to lose. Moses tore off his fine clothes, wrapped himself in a cloak and fled for his life! When he had gone some distance, he stopped and took one last look back at the palace. From now on life for him would be very different.

For many years Moses lived and worked as a shepherd, in a country called Midian. He was married with a family and his sons helped him look after the sheep and goats. Imagine the stories Moses must have told his children about his own childhood; not many shepherds could say they had once been rescued by a princess and had lived in a palace!

Moses might have gone on living in Midian with his family for many more years. But one day, a strange thing happened . . .

Moses had taken some sheep to feed on the slopes of Mount Sinai. He was alone that day, keeping a look-out for wild animals – wolves and lions often lurked behind rocks, waiting to attack a stray lamb. As he shielded his eyes from the sun, Moses saw a bush which *appeared* to be on fire. So he took a closer look. Although the bush was glowing with flames, the branches were not burnt at all. It was very puzzling. Moses was scratching his chin and wondering about it when a voice called to him out of the fire.

"Moses! Moses!"

Moses jumped back in surprise. Somehow he just *knew* it was God speaking to him and he replied in a trembling voice,

"Yes, here I am."

"Take off your shoes," said God. "You are standing on holy ground."

Moses obeyed at once and waited to hear what God would say next.

"I know how unhappy the Israelites are in Egypt," said God. "So I want YOU to help me rescue them. You must go back to Egypt and lead my people to their own land – the land I promised to give them long ago."

But Moses didn't like the idea of going back to Egypt one bit, so he tried to make an excuse.

"Oh, no! not me," he said. "I'm just a shepherd. I can look after sheep and goats but I'm not very good with people and . . ."

"I'll be with you," said God. "I'll help you and tell you what to do."

"Oh, please, *please* choose someone else," begged Moses.

He pleaded with God to change his mind but God wouldn't budge. He knew Moses could do the job. But God could see how worried Moses was, so he did something quite extraordinary to encourage him.

He looked at Moses standing
there with his shepherd's crook –
the Bible calls it a 'rod' – and said,
"What are you holding in your hand?"

"A rod," replied Moses.

"Throw it on the ground," said God.

So Moses threw it on the ground and . . . it turned into a
SNAKE! Well, Moses nearly jumped out of his skin.

"Now pick it up by the tail," said God.

Moses felt a bit nervous but he bent down and caught the snake by the tail. Straightaway the snake turned back into a rod again. Moses began to understand how powerful God was.

"Take your rod with you to Egypt," said God. "You will use it to show Pharaoh I am much more powerful than the gods he worships. And you'll meet your brother Aaron again. He will go with you to Egypt."

Moses was glad to hear about his brother. After all, Aaron was much better at talking to people than he was! Moses knew he must obey God, so he went home and told his family what had happened. Not long afterwards Moses, his wife and their children loaded up their donkeys for the long trek – his special mission to Egypt had begun!

Psalm 23

This psalm describes God as a shepherd. A good shepherd looks after his sheep, leading them to the best grass and protecting them from harm, and God looks after his people in just the same way.

God is my shepherd; I have everything I need.

He takes me to fields of green grass and leads me

to quiet pools of fresh water.

He gives me new strength

and he shows me what is right.

Even if I go through the deepest darkness,

I will not be afraid, because God is with me.

Like a good shepherd he will protect me.

I know that God's goodness and love will be with me all my life;

and his house will be my home as long as I live.

Frogs, Flies and Locusts!

One cold, clear night in the desert Moses stood outside his tent under a starry sky. His wife Zipporah, and their children were inside the tent, wrapped in rugs and sleeping soundly. They had been travelling along the rough and dusty road to Egypt for days. During the day the sun beat down and made them hot. At night the air was freezing cold.

Now, as Moses stood in the moonlight, he pulled his cloak more tightly around him. Moses had been used to staying awake at night as a shepherd, guarding his sheep and goats. But tonight he wasn't looking out for prowling wild animals. God had told him that he would meet his brother Aaron on the way to Egypt, and he was anxious not to miss him. Moses kept watch for hours but he saw no one.

At dawn next morning, he peered along the stony track. What was that? Moses thought he could see someone moving in the distance. He rubbed his tired eyes and looked again. Yes! A man was walking towards their camp. Moses waved, and the man shouted a cheerful greeting. It was Aaron, coming to meet his brother, just as God had promised.

The rest of the journey seemed to go more quickly. Aaron and Moses had lots to talk about after so many years apart. And, of course, Moses told his brother all that God had said, about freeing the Israelites from slavery, and leading them to a land of their own. As they walked, they planned how this should be done.

"First, we must call the Israelite leaders together," said Aaron, "and tell them what's going on."

So, when they reached Egypt, Aaron spoke to the Israelites. The leaders believed Aaron and his brother had been sent by God, and they cheered like anything to think they would soon be free. That was the easy part. Moses and Aaron knew the next step would be much harder.

"We must ask Pharaoh to let the Israelites go," said Moses.

I should explain that this was not the same pharaoh Moses had run away from all those years ago. By this time Egypt was ruled by a new pharaoh, and he agreed to see the two brothers. As before, Aaron did the talking.

"The God of Israel says you are to set his people free," he said boldly.

Pharaoh was not amused. In fact, he was very angry.

"What!" he cried. "Who is this god of yours? I don't know anything about him. No! I WON'T let the Israelites go! Besides, I need them to make bricks."

It was true. Pharaoh needed thousands and thousands of bricks to build beautiful temples and buildings.

Brickmaking was hard and messy work. First the slaves had to dig out sticky mud and mix it with water. Then they trod it in or stirred it to make a soft mixture – a bit like making pastry! When the muddy mix was ready, they shaped it into bricks and left them in the sun to bake hard.

The clever Egyptians had also discovered that they could make bricks stronger by adding chopped straw to the mud. They had always given the slaves the straw to work with until that day when Moses and Aaron went to see Pharaoh. He was hopping mad with them for even asking him to free the Israelites to worship God. He thought it was just an excuse for them to have some time off work. So now he made a new rule which would make them work even harder.

"From today," he ordered, "slaves are to go into the fields and . . . CUT THEIR OWN STRAW. But they must still make as many bricks in a day as before."

It was an impossible task and, when the slaves didn't make enough bricks, they were beaten. No wonder the Israelites turned angrily on Moses and Aaron, and blamed God for their troubles.

"We thought God was supposed to be helping us," they said. "He's only made things worse!"

Moses was as upset as they were, and he spoke to God about it.

"Listen," said God. "Tell Pharaoh that unless he sets my people free, some terrible things will happen!"

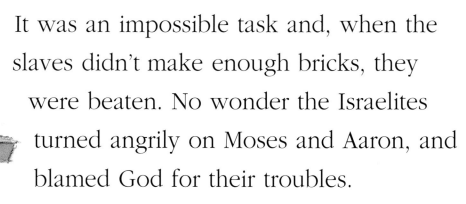

Then God told Moses to wait by the River Nile, where Pharaoh walked each morning. He also reminded Moses to take his rod, which he would use to prove God's powers. Sure enough, next morning, Pharaoh came along with some courtiers. Moses stepped forward and said,

"Your Majesty. God has sent me to tell you to let the Israelites go. If you don't, you'll regret it."

Well, Pharaoh and his courtiers just laughed. Which was a mistake. Moses took his rod, held it out over the river and . . . *SMACK!* he struck the water once. Immediately it turned into thick, red liquid – like blood. No one could drink it. All the fish in the river died and, believe me, the smell of rotting fish was awful.

"Pooh! What a pong!" said Pharaoh.

But he was a stubborn man and still wouldn't change his mind. So a week later, God told Aaron to hold *his* rod over the river. This time hundreds and hundreds of . . . FROGS came hopping out! They hopped into people's houses and jumped all over the palace. Pharaoh was furious.

"Tell your god to take the frogs away," he told Aaron. "*Then* I'll let your people go."

Well, God kept his side of the bargain, but I'm afraid Pharaoh didn't. The frogs went, and the Israelites stayed. After that God made all kinds of dreadful things happen . . .

He sent plagues of gnats, followed by swarms of filthy flies. They bit, buzzed and bothered everybody, and all the animals.

After the insects had gone, a dreadful disease swept through the land. It killed the cattle, camels, horses, donkeys, sheep and goats belonging to the Egyptians. Then people came out in painful boils.

They had just recovered from those disasters when God sent a terrible storm. Thunder boomed and lightning struck the ground. Worse still, hailstones as big as conkers pelted down and flattened all the crops. When that was over thousands of locusts came and settled on the land. They ate *everything* – down to the last blade of grass.

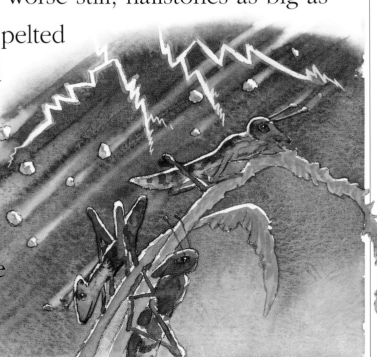

In a while, as if things weren't bad enough, God made thick black clouds drift across the sky. They blotted out the sun and, for three days, the whole of Egypt was plunged into darkness. No one could see a thing.

By this time Moses and Aaron were very fed up. After each disaster, they had been to Pharaoh and begged him to change his mind. Each time he *promised* that if God took away the plague, he would let the Israelites go. But each time, once the trouble was over, he broke his word and refused to set them free.

So God told Moses he would send one more plague – the worst yet. At midnight, every first-born child in Egypt would die! Only the children of Israelite families would survive.

The Israelites were to prepare for what was to come in a special way. Every family had to roast a lamb for supper that evening, cooked with herbs and eaten with flat or 'unleavened' bread – bread made without yeast. God knew the Israelites would have to leave in such a hurry, there wouldn't be enough time for them to use yeast in the bread-dough and wait for it to rise.

They also had to smear the doors of their houses with blood so that God would know which homes to pass over. The children inside *those* houses would be safe from the plague.

Today, Jewish families celebrate the festival of Passover once a year. They eat roasted lamb with unleavened bread to remind them of the first Passover night long ago.

After God had finished speaking, Moses called the leaders together and told them what to do. Everyone obeyed and, as night fell, the Israelites sat down to supper and waited . . .

The children of one Israelite family were excited and, a little afraid at the same time. How strange to be indoors eating a meal, wearing their outdoor clothes!

"Moses says we must be ready to leave Egypt as soon as he tells us," explained their mother. "God will pass over our house tonight and keep us safe. But tomorrow, we may have to leave quickly!"

When it was time for bed, she kissed the children goodnight. Then both she and her husband thanked God that their eldest daughter, Rebecca, would not be killed in the plague. I think they would have been sad too, knowing that many others would die.

At midnight the terrible plague began. The quietness of the night was broken with dreadful cries as the Egyptians discovered their first-born children had died. Not one Egyptian house was spared – even Pharaoh's eldest son was dead. Pharaoh wailed loudest of all.

"Send Moses and Aaron to me at once!" he commanded.

So in the middle of the night the two brothers hurried to the palace. They found Pharaoh grief-stricken.

"Get your people out of my country!" he said angrily. "Go away and leave us in peace!"

And this time he meant it. Moses and Aaron rushed off to spread the good news.

"Pack up your things and get ready!" they shouted. "We're leaving Egypt forever!"

Crossing the Red Sea

"Rebecca, wake up! Wake up!" shouted her mother. "Help me get things ready. We must go!"

It was early in the morning but soon everyone inside that Israelite house I told you about was wide awake and busy. Rebecca helped her younger brother and sister to dress, while her mother rolled up rugs. Then together they tied pots, pans, food and clothes – as much as they could carry – in bundles. Rebecca's father was outside loading up their donkey.

Rebecca lived in a city called Rameses. Ever since Moses and Aaron had said that Pharaoh had given his permission for the Israelites to leave Egypt, people had rushed to get ready. The streets were noisy with excited, chattering families, and their animals. It seemed as if everyone was on the move, carrying babies and belongings. They were off to Canaan, a land which had been promised to them by God.

It wasn't long before Rebecca and her family were ready too. They joined a crowd walking down a road that led out of the city.

Suddenly an Egyptian woman ran out of her house and gave something to Rebecca. It was a gold necklace!

"Hurry away," pleaded the woman. "We don't want any more trouble from you or your god!"

The Egyptians had coped with enough plagues to last a lifetime. No wonder they were glad to see the Israelites go! And many more gave the Israelites jewellry or beautiful materials, to send them on their way.

Moses led his people away from the city. His sister Miriam was walking with him. Strange to think that she had watched over Moses in the bulrushes, when he was just a baby. Now Moses was caring for her, and they were leaving Egypt together.

"Where are we going?" she asked.

"Across the desert to the Red Sea," said Moses.

"How will we find our way?" asked Miriam. "There's no road. Not even a path. We'll get lost!"

"Don't worry," said Moses. "God will guide us. Look. See that cloud swirling above us? It's a sign from God and it will show us the way."

He was right. The strange cloud appeared in front of the Israelites during the daytime and at night God made a pillar of fire to guide them. It was comforting to see the fire, glowing in the dark.

Meanwhile, back in the city, Pharaoh was having second thoughts about letting the Israelites go. Some days had gone by since that terrible night when all the Egyptian first-born children had died. Now the Israelites had gone there were no slaves to do the work. One morning, Pharaoh sent for the captain of his army.

"Bring the Israelites back!" he ordered. "Take your horses and chariots and go after them. They can't have gone far."

As it happened, Moses and his people had
reached the Red Sea, and had set up camp among
the sand dunes nearby. Late one afternoon, Miriam
was walking along a ridge when she spotted a cloud of
dust on the horizon. A sandstorm! she thought. I must warn Moses.

Moses went to look for himself and quickly realised his sister
had been mistaken. The glint of armour in the sunlight and the
sound of horses' hooves pounding across the desert told him that
this was no sandstorm. It was Pharaoh's army – and it was heading
straight for their camp!

Of course, everyone blamed Moses for putting them in danger.

"What are we going to do now?" they said. "We're trapped between the desert and the sea. There's no escape!"

"Keep calm," said Moses. "God is here. He'll save us."

It was difficult to see how, but the Israelites had no choice. They had to trust Moses. The army was getting nearer and nearer. Now they could see soldiers in their war-chariots – the sight was terrifying.

Then God made some amazing things happen. First, the special cloud which had guided Moses changed shape. It hung like a thick curtain of darkness between the Israelites and the army. The Egyptian soldiers couldn't see anything. It gave the Israelites enough time to pack up their belongings and gather on the seashore.

Next, God sent a strong east wind to blow across the sea. He told Moses to lift his rod over the water. When Moses did that the wind howled and blew with such force that it whipped the waters apart – making a pathway *through* the sea! It was a miracle.

"Quick!" shouted Moses above the noise of the wind. "Follow me."

It took all night for the Israelites to walk from one side of the Red Sea to the other. Remember, there were thousands of people and all their animals. By early next morning, the last few stragglers were safely across.

And not before time! When Moses looked back, he saw the Egyptians giving chase. The captain of the army was charging along the shore in his chariot. He had discovered the Israelites' escape route and ordered his men to follow.

But when they were all half-way across, disaster struck. The pathway through the sea was muddy. Soon the chariot wheels clogged and got stuck. The soldiers panicked and whipped their horses but it was no good. The captain was furious. He was desperate to capture the slaves and take them back to Pharaoh. They *must* go on! Then he saw Moses on the far bank, raising his rod over the sea . . .

Suddenly the tide turned. Huge waves rolled and crashed back across the path, and the Egyptian army was drowned. The Israelites had been saved.

Later, as the men folk were putting up tents for the night, Miriam sang a song about what had happened. Other women joined in too – Rebecca and her mother may have been among them – playing their tambourines and dancing with happiness:

"Sing to God,
because he has helped us.
He has thrown Pharaoh's soldiers
into the sea!"

Psalm 121

Who can I turn to when I'm in trouble? asks the writer of this psalm. It reminds us that God is always there to help and protect all those who trust him.

I look up to see the mountains
where my help will come from.
My help will come from God,
who made heaven and earth.

God will not let me fall,
he is always awake.
God never dozes or sleeps,
he is by my side to protect me.

The sun will not hurt me in the daytime,
nor the moon at night.
God will protect me from all danger
and he will keep me safe for ever.

Joshua and the Battle of Jericho

The Israelites spent many years wandering about in the desert. When Moses was an old man he died, and God chose Joshua to become the new leader of the Israelites. It was his job to take God's chosen people to Canaan, the country God promised they should have. They were now nearly there, and only the wide, fast-flowing River Jordan separated the Israelites from their promised land.

Joshua stood on the riverbank and looked across the water to Canaan. He could see vineyards full of grapes and crops of every kind growing in the fields. Everywhere looked fresh and green. This is a fine country! he thought. And so it was.

In the distance Joshua could see Jericho – a beautiful city, which was ruled by the Egyptians. He knew that before the Israelites could claim this country for themselves they would have to capture Jericho. The city was surrounded by thick walls, with towers and battlements which were guarded by soldiers, day and night. Joshua knew the battle for Jericho wouldn't be easy. An attack had to be carefully planned . . .

At that time, a woman called Rahab lived in Jericho. Her house was built into one of the outer walls, just by the city gate. She earned a living by providing food and drink to the many merchants and travellers who came to Jericho each day. She had a large room which opened on to the street. It was always full of noisy, chattering customers, and Rahab got to hear all the latest gossip from them.

Now for some time there had been talk of an invasion. People living in Canaan had heard that the Israelites were camped by the River Jordan, and were planning to invade their country by force! When the news spread to Jericho, Rahab worried about the danger to herself and her family.

"What will happen to us?" she asked a spice merchant one morning. "I've heard the Israelites are a fierce lot."

"Goodness knows!" said the man. "We may all be killed."

"Not if we can help it," said some soldiers who had been listening. "We've been told to keep a look-out for two Israelite spies. They've been spotted in the city snooping around and asking questions. If you see or hear anything, let us know."

That same evening, after dark, two strangers knocked on Rahab's door. As soon as she saw them she felt sure they were the spies the soldiers had told her about! At first she was frightened, because she was alone in the house. But the strangers spoke in a friendly way, and begged her to let them in. They seemed nice enough, so she agreed.

"Quick! Come inside and shut the door," she said. "Pharaoh's soldiers are looking for you."

"We know," said the men anxiously. "Will you help us?"

Rahab nodded. "Follow me," she said. "You can hide on my roof under some flax."

In those days people used flax plants for making linen. They dried the stems on their flat roofs, ready for weaving. Rahab gathered up some bundles, and told the men to cover themselves with it. Suddenly they heard horses' hooves clattering along the street, followed by a loud banging on Rahab's door.

"Open up! Open up!" yelled a voice.

Rahab ran downstairs and opened it. A group of soldiers on horseback stood outside. The captain asked if she had seen the two spies.

"Yes," said Rahab. "They were here earlier, but they left by the city gate before sunset. You'll catch them if you ride fast."

Because the soldiers knew Rahab well they believed her, and galloped away. When they had gone she ran upstairs to the roof.

"You must escape over the wall," she said to the spies. "Hurry, before the soldiers come back!"

As they got ready to leave, the two men thanked Rahab for helping them.

They told her they had been sent by their leader Joshua, to find out how well the city was defended. They warned her that the Israelites planned to attack Jericho, very soon.

When Rahab heard this she was terrified.

"I've saved your lives," she said. "*Please*, spare me and my family in the battle."

The spies promised she wouldn't be harmed, and told her what to do.

"Before the battle," they said, "bring every member of your family into the house. Then tie a red cord outside the window. It will be a sign that everyone in your house is to be saved."

Afterwards Rahab lowered the men down the high city wall, on a rope. When they were down the two spies raced back to Joshua to tell him all they had seen.

Back at the camp the Israelites were excited. Joshua had told them to pack up their tents and wait for his command to cross the river. Don't forget there were thousands of men, women and children in his care, not to mention all their animals! But God had told him how to get everyone safely across. Also by this time Joshua had organised the strongest men among them into an army, so he called his officers together and explained the plan.

"The priests will carry the Ark of the Covenant down to the water's edge," he said.

The Ark of the Covenant was a special golden box. It contained two pieces of stone, which had God's ten commandments written on them. The Ark was very precious to the Israelites, because it reminded them that God was with his people, and they carried it with them wherever they went.

"As soon as the priests step into the river with the Ark," Joshua went on, "the water will stop flowing. A dry pathway will appear and everyone will be able to walk to the other side."

When the time came, the Israelites waited with Joshua on the banks of the River Jordan. They watched as four priests carried the Ark down to the water . . .

Then everything happened just as Joshua said it would. The river dried up, and the Israelites walked into Canaan. They had reached the Promised Land at last.

So far, so good, thought Joshua. Now for Jericho!

Straightaway Joshua worked on a battle plan. He knew the city had huge walls and that the gates would be barred against him. How *would* they get in? He was still worrying about that problem when a messenger came to him. He said he'd been sent by God, and told Joshua how to capture the city. His orders sounded a bit strange but, when the messenger had gone, Joshua called his men together.

"Do exactly as I say," he told them. "In seven days the walls of Jericho will come tumbling down, you'll see!"

And this is how it happened.

Day one: Joshua and his army marched once round the city walls on the outside – in silence. Seven priests led the procession, blowing trumpets made from rams' horns. The Ark of the Covenant was carried behind.

Day two: They did it again.

Day three: And again.

How peculiar! thought everyone living in the city. And they waited to see what Joshua would do next.

Day four: The same as days one, two and three. Silent marching, except for the priests with trumpets blowing. Nothing more.

Day five: Guess what? More of the same.

Day six: Repeat instructions, as for the last five days.

By now, the people of Jericho were laughing at the Israelites. They thought Joshua didn't know how to fight. Which was a mistake because, on *day seven . . .* Joshua and his army marched round the city seven times. The seven priests blew on their trumpets and, when Joshua gave the word, his people gave a great SHOUT! The noise of that terrible shout was so loud that the walls of Jericho crumbled and fell with a deafening *crash!*

Then Joshua led his army over the rubble and killed all the people in the city. Only Rahab and her family were saved, because Joshua saw the red cord tied to her window, and he remembered how she had helped his spies.

And that is the amazing story of how Joshua won the battle of Jericho.

Strong Man Samson

This story is all about a man called Samson. When he was born God told his mother that he would grow to be a very strong man. He had made Samson strong so he could fight the Philistines – who were enemies of the Israelites.

"But you must never cut his hair," said God. "If you do, he will lose his strength."

In time Samson grew to be the strongest man around and, of course, his hair grew with him. He never ever cut it or told anyone the secret of his strength. Once, while he was out walking, he killed a lion with his bare hands. You see how strong he was.

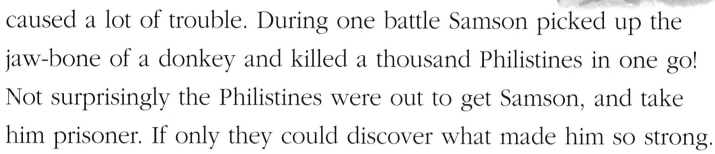

He fought and killed many Philistines too. They were fierce people from another country who had invaded Canaan. They quarrelled with the Israelites over who should have the land and caused a lot of trouble. During one battle Samson picked up the jaw-bone of a donkey and killed a thousand Philistines in one go! Not surprisingly the Philistines were out to get Samson, and take him prisoner. If only they could discover what made him so strong.

By chance Samson fell in love with a beautiful woman called Delilah. She made Samson very happy and he would have done anything for her. It wasn't long before the Philistines got to hear about Delilah. They thought they might persuade her to help them. Imagine Delilah's surprise when five Philistine lords came visiting, and offered her lots of money.

"We'll each give you eleven hundred pieces of silver," they said, "if you can find out the secret of Samson's strength."

Well, five times eleven hundred pieces of silver was a small fortune! So Delilah agreed. Besides, it didn't seem much to ask. She was sure she could charm Samson into telling her his secret. One evening she arranged for the Philistines to hide close enough to hear, while she spoke softly to Samson.

"If someone wanted to capture you," she asked, "how would they do it?'

"They'd have to tie me up with seven new bowstrings," said Samson. "That should do the trick."

Later, while he was asleep, Delilah tied him up with the bowstrings. Then she shouted, "Samson! The Philistines are here!"

Samson woke with a start, and finding his arms bound with bowstrings he broke them one by one. *Ping, ping, ping!* They snapped like rubber bands. Then Delilah knew he hadn't been telling her the truth. So, another evening she asked him again. This time Samson told her,

"I would have to be held by new ropes," he said. "Only ropes that had never been used would be strong enough to hold me."

Again Delilah waited until he was asleep before she tied him up. Then she shouted, "Samson! The Philistines are here!"

Samson woke up and *snap, snap, snap!*

He broke the ropes easily, as if they were nothing more than cotton threads. When Delilah saw that Samson had lied to her again, she wanted to know why.

"If you love me," she said, "you should tell the truth."

She pleaded with Samson to tell her how he could be weakened.

"Well," he said, "you would have to weave my hair into your loom. If you did that, you'd make me weak."

The next night Delilah wove Samson's hair into her weaving loom while he slept. Again she shouted, "Samson! The Philistines are here!"

To her great surprise Samson sprang up and freed himself from the loom, as strong as ever.

"Where are these Philistines?" he demanded. "I'll fight them all with one hand behind my back!"

Now Delilah was really angry. She tried everything she could think of to make Samson tell her his secret. She cried, wheedled, nagged and pestered him until Samson could bear it no longer. He loved Deliliah very much, so this time he told her the truth.

"If you . . . CUT MY HAIR," he said, "I shall lose my strength. That is true, I promise."

When he was asleep Delilah signalled to the Philistines hiding nearby and *snip, snip, snip!* They cut off Samson's hair. As soon as it was done, Delilah shouted once more, "Samson! The Philistines are here!"

As Samson leapt to attack them he saw his hair piled on the floor. Too late! The Philistines grabbed his arms, and took him prisoner. And Samson, who had been the strongest man ever, was too weak to struggle.

The Philistines were very cruel to Samson. They blinded him, shackled his legs with chains and threw him into prison. Every day they chained him to a mill wheel and made him work like an ox, grinding corn. But while he was in prison, Samson's hair began to grow . . . and you can guess what that meant, can't you?

One day the Philistines were having a big celebration in honour of their god, Dagon. The temple was packed full of people chanting, singing and dancing – and there were thousands more on the roof. In the middle of all this commotion someone thought it would be fun to drag Samson out of prison, so they could all jeer at their old enemy. Soon the cry went up, "We want Samson! We want Samson!"

Before long, Samson was brought into the temple and everyone mocked him. He looked a sorry sight as he stood, head bowed, between two enormous pillars.

By now Samson's hair had grown long, and it fell round his shoulders like a cape. While the Philistines laughed and spat at him, Samson prayed. He asked God to give him back his strength, just once more. Then he braced himself between the two pillars and pushed with all his might. Yes! He could feel his strength returning . . .

"We shall all die together!" he cried.

Then Samson *push, push, PUSHED!* until the pillars cracked and crumbled. The Philistines' jeers turned to screams as massive blocks of stone came hurtling down on top of them. The temple roof fell in, and everyone was killed.

Poor Samson died too, crushed beneath the ruins. God had given him back his strength to fight his enemies. And you may like to know that Samson killed more Philistines on that day, than in his whole lifetime!

Wise King Solomon

You remember the story of David and Goliath? Well, many years after David had killed the giant, he became king. When David died his son, Solomon, took his place as king of Israel.

King Solomon was a good and wise king. Like his father David, he trusted in God and tried hard to please him. And, because God was pleased with Solomon, he granted him his wish to be wise, so that he could rule his people fairly.

Sometimes when there were arguments, people came to Solomon to sort them out. One day two young mothers came to the palace with a baby. They looked very upset.

"What's the matter?" asked Solomon.

The women told him that they shared a house. They had both had babies at about the same time, but one of the babies had died. Now, each mother was claiming the living baby as her own.

"She stole my baby!" cried one woman. "She crept into my room while I was asleep and took him away."

"I didn't, I didn't!" shouted the other. "He's my baby and you know it!"

Solomon listened as the two mothers quarrelled angrily. Then the baby woke up and started crying. So the king thought of a clever way to find out which mother was telling the truth.

"Bring me my sword," he said to one of his servants. "I'll chop the baby in half! Then each mother will have half a child."

The woman who had spoken first agreed.

"Good idea!" she said. "That way neither of us will have him."

"No!" screamed the second mother. "Don't kill my baby. I would rather give him away than see him killed."

That settled it! Solomon knew at once that the second woman was telling the truth. Without a doubt, she was the *real* mother and he gave her the child. Do you know why? Solomon knew that the real mother would protect her baby at all costs, even if it meant giving the child away. You see how wise he was.

Solomon wrote many words of wisdom. His wise sayings were about choosing right from wrong, about children and their parents and everyday life. He also wrote many beautiful songs and poems about birds, animals and plants.

As well as being wise, King Solomon was a good ruler. To begin with he knew it was important to defend his country from invaders, so he made sure his troops were well-trained and equipped with weapons.

At that time the best way for the Israelites to attack their enemies was in war chariots. The two-wheeled, horse-drawn chariots could race across the flat plains quickly, and head off an approaching army. The bigger, four-wheeled chariots were slower, but they could carry more fighting men.

Some chariots had teams of three men: the driver, a bowman and one armed with a shield and spear.

Solomon built up a huge force of chariots, horses and charioteers (as chariot drivers were called), which were kept ready for action at all times. It was a costly business. Hundreds of men worked at building and repairing the chariots. Horses had to be bought, trained and looked after, not to mention the cost of keeping twelve thousand charioteers! Add to this the cost of building good roads for the chariots to speed along – and you can imagine how much money was needed to pay for it all.

King Solomon raised money by charging his people taxes, and by trading with other countries. Merchants who travelled through Israel to sell their goods had to pay a toll. Shipping was also very important in those days. Merchant ships sailed far and wide carrying spices, gold and bronze, but they needed safe harbours where they could unload their cargoes. Solomon saw a clever way to make more money by building safe harbours, or ports along the coast. Every time a ship docked in one of his ports, the captain had to pay a large fee!

Solomon became one of the wealthiest kings ever, and used his money wisely. He built a fleet of ships and became the first king of Israel to own a merchant navy. He bought many beautiful things and, during his lifetime, spent a fortune on buildings, and a palace for his wife. But by far the most important thing to him was to build a temple to God, in Jerusalem.

It took about seven years to build Solomon's Temple, and many thousands of slaves and craftsmen were brought together to work on it. Tons of stone for the walls had to be quarried and made into blocks. Cedar trees from Lebanon were cut and shipped down the coast on rafts. This sweet-smelling wood was used for the inside walls, which were carved with flowers and trees and painted with pure gold.

The finished Temple was magnificent. It had a big entrance porch, a main hall and a room called the Holy of Holies. On the day the Temple was dedicated to God, there were great celebrations in Jerusalem. The priests carried the Ark of the Covenant into the Holy of Holies, where it would always be kept.

And when Solomon asked God for his blessing, the Bible says God filled the Temple with a cloud of glory, to show how pleased he was. There had never been a wiser king to rule the land of Israel.

Psalm 148

The message in this happy psalm is for everything in the world to praise God. The writer has thought of everything from the sun, moon and stars to monsters in the sea . . . not forgetting old people and children too!

Praise God in the heavens;
praise him, all his angels.
Praise him, sun and moon;
praise him, shining stars.

Praise God from the earth;
and all oceans and sea-monsters.
Lightning, hail, snow and clouds,
and strong winds all obey him.

Praise God, green hills and high mountains,
fruit-trees, jungles and forests.
Praise him, tame and wild animals
and all reptiles and birds.

Praise God, kings and queens
and all other rulers.
Praise him, young men and women
old people and children too.

Let us all praise God!

The Queen of Sheba

The Queen of Sheba was rich and beautiful. She had heard all about King Solomon from people who had visited Jerusalem. They told her wonderful tales about his wisdom and wealth.

"You should see his palace!" said some. "It's full of gold and ivory."

"Solomon is amazing," said others. "He writes songs and wise sayings *and* he rules his country well."

The queen was sure such a wise man could tell her many things and give her good advice, so she decided to visit him. She told her attendants to prepare for the long journey to Jerusalem.

"How far is Jerusalem?" one of them asked the queen.

"More than a thousand miles, I should say," she said. "It will take us weeks to get there."

Now the queen wanted to impress Solomon, so she decided to give him lots of expensive presents.

For a start, there were huge bundles of spices. Nutmeg, cinnamon, cloves and peppercorns were all important spices for flavouring food. They cost a lot of money. In those days peppercorns, for instance, were more valuable than gold, so you can imagine how much whole sacks-full would cost!

Next, there were boxes full of fabulous jewels – jade from China, and other precious gemstones, as well as a large amount of gold. And, as if these gifts were not enough, the queen ordered a cargo of juniper wood to be sent in ships to Solomon.

Soon servants were rushing about loading spices, jewels and gold on to camels. Tents, rugs, food and water had to be carried too – things the queen and her attendants would need on such a long journey. At last everything was ready.

As the sun rose one morning, the royal 'caravan', as a group of people travelling together was called, left for Jerusalem. The Queen of Sheba was on her way!

Day after day the caravan made its way along dusty tracks, across deserts and over hills. The camels walked at a steady pace.

Plod, plod, plod. Mile after mile. *Plod, plod, plod.* Each evening everyone set up camp for the night. Then at sunrise they were off again, *plod, plod, PLOD!*

Weeks went by until . . . one sunny day in Jersualem, King Solomon was getting ready to greet his royal visitor. A messenger had told him that the Queen of Sheba had just arrived at the city gates. He was curious to meet this adventurous queen, who had travelled so far to see him.

News of the queen's arrival spread quickly through the city and crowds came to watch her. She looked splendid as she rode through the streets, dressed in her finest robes. When she reached the palace, trumpets sounded a fanfare and Solomon came out to welcome her.

The Queen of Sheba was very glad to see Solomon at last. First, she presented him with all those gifts I told you about – spices, jewels, gold and juniper wood. He was *very* pleased with them! And because the king was fond of music, he had some of the juniper made into beautiful musical instruments, such as harps.

Later, when they were alone, the queen couldn't wait to ask Solomon lots of questions. She wanted to know about so *many* things!

Solomon laughed.

"Questions, questions, questions!" he said.

But he answered all of them wisely.

"Everything I have heard about you is true," said the queen. "But you are even wiser and wealthier than I have been told."

That night Solomon gave a magnificent feast in her honour. The tables in the banqueting hall were spread with delicious food which they ate off plates of gold. While they feasted, the king and queen were entertained by fine musicians and dancing girls.

In the days that followed, the queen learned how good
Solomon was at ruling his country, and that he tried to please God.
The Bible says the queen was breathless and amazed at everything
she learned about Solomon.

"No wonder you are king of Israel!" she said.

When it was time to go, the king gave her many lovely gifts. Perhaps he wrote some songs for her too. Then the Queen of Sheba returned home. It had been a marvellous time, and one she would remember for the rest of her life!